THE WORLD OF THE FUTURE
ROBOTS
SCIENCE & MEDICINE INTO THE 21st CENTURY

CREDITS

The cover shows a three-legged exploration robot walking in the jungles of an alien world.

The previous page shows a multi-armed assembly robot building a space station with parts taken into orbit by a Space Shuttle rocket.

This page shows a group of robots erecting the domes of a planetary base. By the time the human explorers arrive, their living quarters will be warmed and comfortable.

Written by
Kenneth Gatland and
David Jefferis
Designed and produced by
David Jefferis Ltd
Illustrated by
Terry Hadler
Brian Lewis
Michael Roffe

Acknowledgements
We wish to thank the following individuals and organizations for their assistance.

Boeing Aerospace Corporation
British Interplanetary Society
Grumman Aerospace
National Geographic Society
McDonnell Douglas Aerospace
NASA
Rockwell Aerospace
TRW Inc
© 1979 Usborne Publishing Ltd

Usborne Publishing Ltd
20 Garrick Street
London WC2E 9BJ

Published in Canada by
Hayes Publishing Ltd
Burlington, Ontario.

Printed in Belgium by
Henri Proost, Turnhout,
Belgium.

THE WORLD OF THE FUTURE
ROBOTS
SCIENCE & MEDICINE INTO THE 21ST CENTURY

INTRODUCTION

This book describes the ideas scientists have for solving the problems, such as the energy crisis and world-wide pollution, that face the human race today.

Robots, intelligent machines using advanced computer systems as their 'brains', will help mankind run an increasingly complex world. Few of them will look like the popular image of a robot – a machine in the shape of a human. The real robots will come in all sorts of shapes and sizes, according to the job they are designed for.

One thing is certain – amazing as many of the ideas in this book are, the *real* world of the future will be more amazing than anyone can imagine.

CONTENTS

3

FROM STONE-AGE TOOLS TO SPACE-AGE COMPUTERS

The history of man has been that of a curious animal learning about the world and changing it to suit itself.

On these pages you can see some of the major inventions that have enabled mankind to become the dominant species on Planet Earth.

With the invention of the atomic bomb, it has become possible for a major war to cause a complete collapse of world-wide civilization.

Let us hope that enough people remember that our ape ancestors first succeeded by co-operating with each other. The lesson should not be forgotten, otherwise there may be no future worth writing or reading about.

Man the toolmaker

The discovery that useful tools like knives and axes could be made by chipping stones and flints dates back at least 250,000 years. Tools like these were not only used for hunting and skinning animals – they were valuable and were used for trading.

The dawn of agriculture

Agriculture was the main way in which primitive man developed toward civilization. Instead of being hunters and nomads, people could settle and build houses, villages and cities. The plough was first used about 5,000 BC. Ones like the primitive type shown are still used in parts of the Middle East.

The birth of science

The foundations of modern science were laid in Ancient Greece during the 500 years before the birth of Christ. The steam turbine shown here was invented a little later by an engineer called Hero, born about 20 AD. When water boiled in the sphere, the escaping steam spun it round on its axle.

4 The invention of gunpowder

The Chinese invented this explosive mixture, using it for rockets and fire arrows as early as 700 AD. It was not used in Europe until five centuries later. The first recorded use of a gun was in the town of Amberg in 1301 and a brass cannon was used at the siege of Metz 23 years later.

5 Observing the invisible

Dutch spectacle maker Zacharias Jansen invented the microscope about 1590. He saw a microscopic world which no-one had known existed. In 1608, another Dutchman, Hans Lippershey, invented the telescope. Galileo Galilei later became famous for his astronomical discoveries using the new invention.

6 Surgery and medicine

Artificial limbs were made as early as the 1500s, but without anaesthetics to make the patient unconscious, surgery was painful and barbaric. The discovery of bacteria led eventually to the life-saving drugs and medicines which are used in hospitals today.

7 Electricity

The light bulb was invented by an American, Thomas Edison, in 1878. This, together with other 19th-century electrical inventions such as the dynamo and motor, changed the world and led to electronic devices like TV and radio. Most homes now have more than 50 electrical devices in them – try counting the ones in your own home.

8 The atomic age

The threat of atomic war has hung over the peoples of the world ever since two bombs were exploded over Hiroshima and Nagasaki in 1945, ending World War II. In 1952, the hydrogen bomb was first exploded. It used the fusion nuclear reaction which powers the Sun. Yet the same power, controlled, could provide cheap and safe electric power.

9 Tele-communications

150 years ago, it took weeks for a message to get from Europe to the USA. Now it takes less than a second using electronic equipment like radio and television. Using the same electronic principles, radar beams sweep the skies, providing an almost instantaneous check on everything in them from storm clouds to atom bombers.

10 Computers

The first electronic computer was called ENIAC and was completed in 1943 Today's transistorized computers are used in everything from cameras to watches. Though only a super-fast adding machine, the computer has some similarities to the human brain and some people think that the computer will eventually far exceed the brain's capacity.

Now read on... into the fantastic world of the future...

PROVIDING FOR A POWER-HUNGRY PLANET

Plentiful energy is the basis of world civilization and future supplies are essential.

At present, oil is used for most energy needs, but supplies are limited, so new sources of energy have to be found.

On these pages, you can see some of the ways in which energy, in the form of electricity, might be generated in the 21st century.

Power from the waves

Salter's Ducks, named after their Scottish inventor Stephen Salter, are teardrop-shaped pods which move up and down in ocean waves like nodding ducks. As they nod, pumps inside them move up and down too, driving power-producing generators.

Prototypes are already being built, and eventually long lines of them may surround the world's coastlines.

The picture shows one of the more hazardous aspects of this non-polluting power source. Engineers struggle to replace a damaged pump unit during a howling North Atlantic gale. Critics of the ducks say that long lines of them would be a hazard to shipping. Also they would affect, perhaps badly, tide and wave patterns.

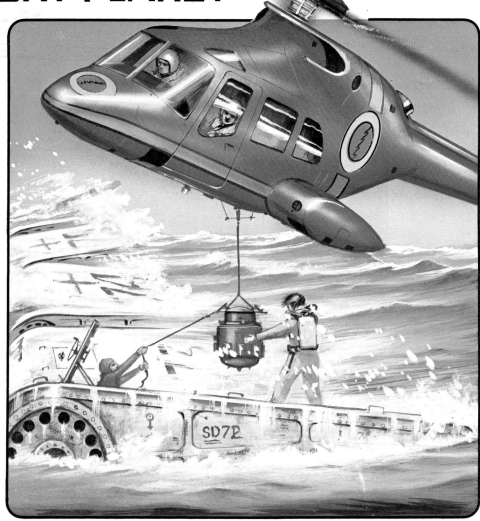

Nuclear fusion

At present, this is the most likely oil replacement. Various types of fusion reactor are under development. The one shown uses laser beams to crush a pellet of deuterium. They crush it until its atoms fuse together – giving off immense heat in the process. The heat is used to turn water to steam, which then spins electric turbines to generate electricity.

An advantage of nuclear fusion is that it produces little radio-active waste unlike present-day fission reactors, some of whose wastes will take centuries before becoming safe. Also, its fuel, deuterium, comes from seawater which is available free and in vast quantities.

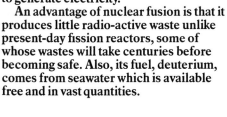

Power from the ocean depths

On the left engineers carry out a repair operation on a giant power station of the future. It uses the difference in temperature between warm surface waters and cool deep waters to generate power.

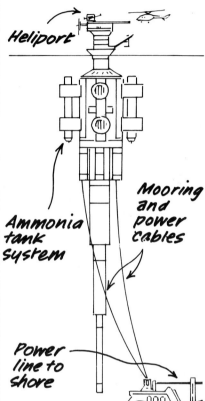

Heliport

Ammonia tank system

Mooring and power cables

Power line to shore

How it works

At the station's core is an ammonia tank. Ammonia needs only a small temperature change to turn from a liquid to a gas and back again.

Warm surface water is pumped around the ammonia tank. As the ammonia warms up it turns into gas. The gas is piped to a turbine, spinning it to generate electricity. Cold water is pumped up from the depths to cool the ammonia, turning it back to a liquid, ready to repeat the cycle once more.

The energy outlook

Energy will be generated by a wide variety of methods in the 21st century. It will be an almost totally electric world, with liquid hydrogen replacing oil as a fuel to power, for example, aircraft and cars.

ENERGY FROM SPACE

The development of solar cells, flat panes of silicon material which convert the energy contained in sunlight to electricity, has enabled scientists to dream up the 'power station in space' idea.

Using solar cells to supply electricity is possible here on Earth – calculators, watches and battery chargers are some of the gadgets now on sale powered by them. The problem is that on very cloudy days and at night the cells do not receive much light, so can supply little or no electricity.

In space, there is a continuous torrent of sunpower, ready for use by the power station in space.

▲ This dumpy-looking spaceship is the Boeing aircraft company's idea of a Heavy Lift Vehicle of the 1990s. With a mighty roar the HLV takes off, loaded with up to 227 tonnes of cargo. Its destination, a 'building site' in orbit.

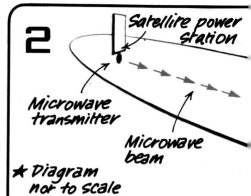

★ Diagram not to scale

The HLV's cargo is helping to build the Satellite Solar Power Station, shown in diagram form above and in the big picture below. The SSPS orbits Earth in almost continuous sunshine. The electricity supplied by its vast panels of

The Solar cycle

Electric motor

This curious tricycle was invented in Germany. The 'sunshade' is in fact a solar-cell panel which powers a small electric motor near the front wheel.

The motor is powerful enough to keep the Solarmobile rolling along on flat roads. Up hills the rider has to help by pedalling and on cloudy days or at night the Solarmobile stays at home as its solar cells do not generate power in the dark.

5 Building an SSPS

Below you can see a Boeing HLV, cargo doors open wide. To the right is a Space Shuttle 'parked' next to the control core of the SSPS. In this design, the kilometres-long SSPS would be built in low Earth orbit, just a few hundred kilometres up. Much of the girder-work construction will be completed by robot 'beam builders' now being developed by the Grumman aerospace company. Once complete, thrust motors would gently push it up and out into a higher orbit, nearly 36,000 km from Earth.

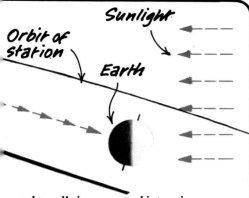

Sunlight

Orbit of station

Earth

solar cells is converted into microwave energy (like a super power radar beam) which is aimed to a receiving station on Earth. The SSPS is in 'geostationary' orbit – one which keeps over the same spot on Earth.

▲ The HLV returns to its Earth base after dumping its cargo in orbit. The landing 'pad' is a giant circular lake on which the HLV splashes down. (It will be designed to float.) After refuelling it will be re-furbished, then will fly again.

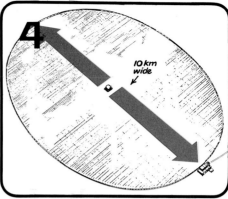

10 km wide

▲ This is the 10 km-wide receiving aerial for the SSPS's microwave beam. At the bottom right you can see the station which converts the microwaves back into electricity, ready to supply the world's power needs.

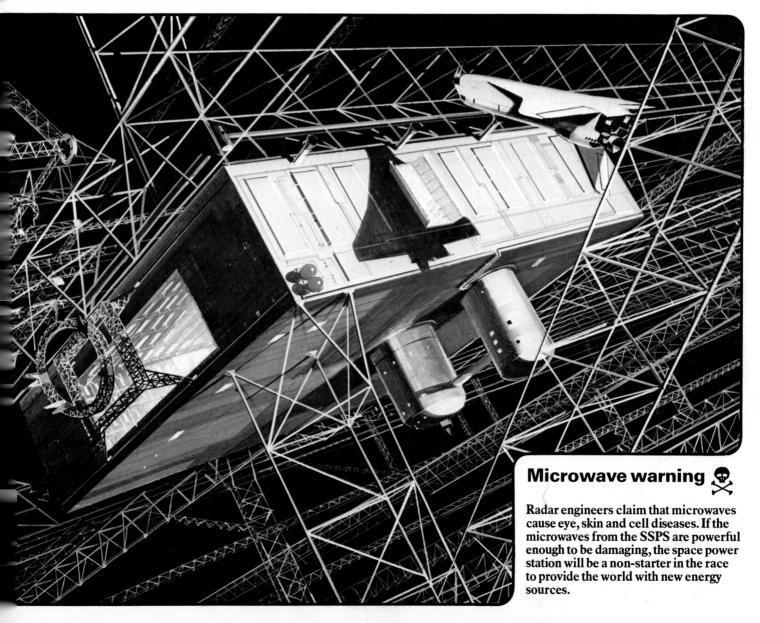

Microwave warning ☠

Radar engineers claim that microwaves cause eye, skin and cell diseases. If the microwaves from the SSPS are powerful enough to be damaging, the space power station will be a non-starter in the race to provide the world with new energy sources.

FACTORIES IN ORBIT

Why make things in space?

The First Industrial Revolution began in England in the 18th century, introducing powered machinery to replace human and animal muscle power.

The Second Industrial Revolution, still going on, began in the USA early this century, replacing human brain-power with automatic control devices, such as computers.

The Third Industrial Revolution has yet to happen. It will be the moving of many industrial operations (particularly polluting ones) away from Earth and into space.

Is this imagination? Many experts think not – their only arguments are about when, not if, it will happen.

The secret of making things in space is that materials float weightless, a condition impossible to achieve on Earth. Materials of great purity melted inside space furnaces can be made free of contact with containers. They include new alloys which will not mix on Earth and foam steels so light they will float on water. Space factories also have direct access to a vacuum – necessary for many industrial processes – and the free energy of sunlight.

Key to Vulcan One, the space factory of the future

Vulcan One, orbiting high above the Earth's surface, is named after the Roman god of metalworkers and fire. The factory is a prototype for other larger ones still in the planning stages back on Earth.
1 A Space Shuttle, doors open, has just been loaded with a module full of space-made (the best) optical glass for use in high quality instruments. By the time Vulcan One is in service, the Shuttle, built several years earlier, will be well used indeed and showing signs of wear and tear. Aerospace engineers will no doubt be planning a replacement.
2 Vulcan One is a unit structure. Each module has been ferried up in the cargo hold of a Shuttle.
3 The command module contains approach radars and control equipment.
4 Solar panels supply power for the factory. Their angle and power output is controlled by the command module.
5 The Earth. Once the Third Industrial Revolution is underway, the pressures on its ecological balance from polluting heavy industry should be eased.
6 Manufacturing modules are plugged into the factory's spine as required. Each one makes a different product.
7 Service engineers keep the factory operating efficiently.
8 Vulcan Two, slightly larger and slightly more advanced, pointing the way to the huge factories of the 1990s and 21st century.
9 Storing finished products is no problem – they are stored in sealed cans in space, anchored with elastic netting.

Some products from Vulcan One

These three products are ones which can be made in space using present-day knowledge. Others will no doubt be developed. Shown below is the equipment used to make urokinase, a medicine for treating unwanted blood clots, which if free in the blood-stream can disable or kill.

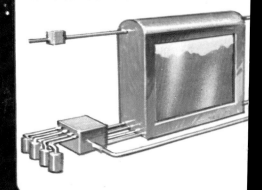

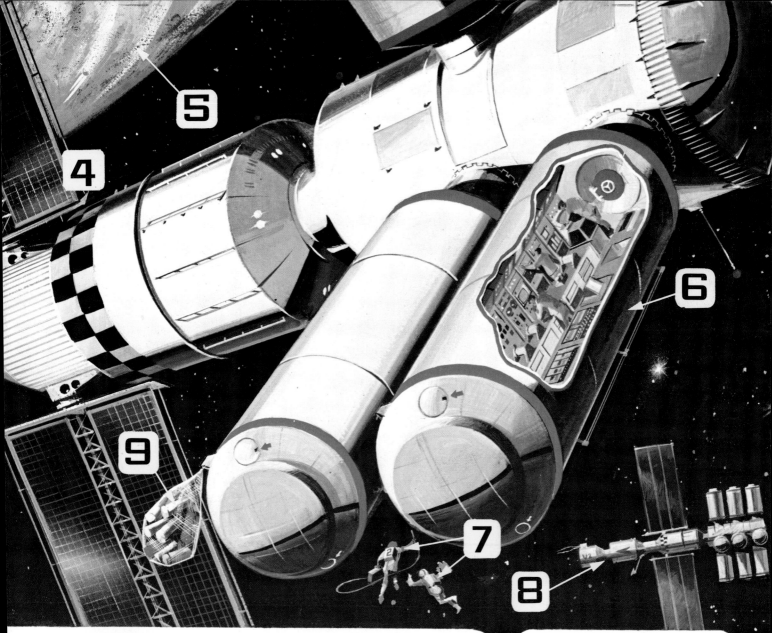

A space oddity

is is the front fan of a jumbo jet engine.
ace-made fan blades would be stronger than
se made on Earth and could withstand
er-high temperatures allowing engines
ng them to operate very efficiently.
e estimate of the fuel saved if space-made
des were used on airliners is an
azing 4,000 million litres a year.

Crystals used in electronic equipment
can be grown large and pure in orbit.
The one photographed above was grown
in Skylab, the American manned space
laboratory, in 1974. The crystal's
size and quality were a huge improvement over ones grown on Earth. Large-
scale manufacturing of crystals in
space ought to make them far cheaper to
make than back on Earth, too.

At left is an earth-bound candle. Hot
air rises over it. Fresh oxygen rushes
in at the base keeping the wick
burning. At right, the weightless
space-candle burns with a
globe-shaped flame. Hot air does not
rise and in a few seconds the candle
uses all the oxygen around it and
seems to go out. But the heat can only
escape by slowly radiating away, and
if the candle is supplied with fresh
oxygen later, it will mysteriously flare
into life again.

GOLD MINES IN THE SKY

Many people foresee doom for technological civilization within the next century as a result of energy shortages, pollution problems and shortages of essential mineral resources.

You have already seen that there need be little reason for energy shortages. Dirty production processes can be taken 'off-planet' into orbit. And for natural resources, there is the mineral wealth of the entire Solar System.

Materials from the Moon, Asteroid Belt and Jupiter could be mined if it becomes necessary in the same way that rigs now drill for oil in the dangerous waters of the North Sea.

Moonminers

This picture shows two moonminers, supported aloft by compressed-gas powered backpacks. They carry electronic equipment designed for mineral surveying.

Down below are the two tracked vehicles they are using as a mobile base (the backpacks carry fuel for just a few minutes flight at a time), while on the right you can see the explosions set off in the lunar crust by other members of the survey team.

From recordings made of the explosions echoing through the lunar rock, the surveyors will be able to tell the composition of the rock in the area and whether it is of value in their quest for minerals.

Once a good site has been chosen, robot equipment will be installed to mine the minerals.

▲ There is no need for expensive rocket power to get materials (such as calcium and aluminium) off the Moon. This long machine does the job. It is an electro-magnetic catapult, which accelerates mineral-carrying modules up to 2,400 metres a second, enough to escape the Moon's gravitational pull.

The modules would be aimed to finish their journeys close to space factories orbiting the Earth.

The catapult's foundations are made of moon-soil bulldozed into position. Power for the electromagnets is provided by solar cells. This base is near the Moon's South Pole where the Sun never sets, so the production of power is constant.

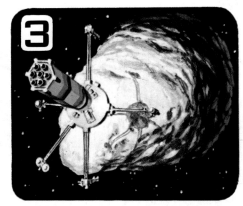

▲ Out in the Asteroid Belt, a prospector ship has a rich find – a kilometre-wide rock ball. When refined in a space factory orbiting Callisto, a moon of Jupiter, it should yield nearly 10 million tonnes of pure iron ore.

▲ An ion-drive engine and navigation system are installed on the rock. The low-thrust engine slowly eases the rock into a new orbit – one that will take it near Callisto, now the capital-world of human colonies in the outer Solar System.

▲ Months (or even years) later, the rock is met and slowed by an automatic collection tug, before being melted down and refined. A steady stream of asteroid rocks provides a constant supply of raw material, mainly iron and nickel, for factories.

▲ Jupiter is larger than all the other planets in the Solar System put together. Its atmosphere contains hydrogen, ammonia and other chemicals in vast quantities. Since Jupiter has no solid surface (its atmosphere just gets thicker and thicker as you go deeper) a hot-air balloon suspended in the upper atmosphere is the best way to mine the planet. Hung below the balloon are the refining and power plants necessary to 'sieve' the atmosphere of its chemical riches. Spacecraft like the one shown are used to carry the material up into space. The system would have to be completely automated – Jupiter has intense radiation belts too dangerous for humans to endure. Other hazards for the robots would include the storms which rage in Jupiter's atmosphere.

LOOKING AFTER OUR WORLD

The best place to keep a watch over the Earth is from space. Satellites are already used to monitor Earth's vital natural resources and in the future their role will become even more varied and important.

'Eyes in space' can keep track of air and sea pollution and give advance warning of floods, drought and forest fires. By using special photographic equipment, pictures can show if crops are diseased or healthy.

There are thousands of man-made objects in orbit. Already space agencies have to plan carefully if they wish to put satellites into popular orbits. In the future, a rationing system may be set to avoid collisions.

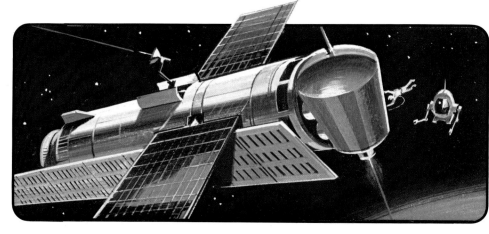

▲ This 14-tonne satellite, which could be in orbit by 1985, is designed to observe pollution and resources. It has two lasers – one above the solar cell 'wings' for communication with other satellites; the other, pointed downwards, is used to check the distance between the satellite and the Earth, enabling the satellite to detect, for example, changes in water level for flood detection and control. The laser distance-checker would be sensitive enough to detect changes of as little as 30 cm

▲ Nearly 36,000 km above the equator, the Meteosat, put in orbit by the European Space Agency, provides a world weather watch. This picture, which shows Africa and South America, was taken on 9 December 1977. Satellites have provided the first means of reliable weather forecasting, even if only – at present – for very short periods ahead. In the future, long-range forecasting should become possible, though reliable ones of just a week ahead would make a good start.

▲ This satellite, shown being serviced by an astronaut-engineer, has a laser to measure the small movements in the Earth's crust which are early indicators of earthquakes. This one is focused on a reflector embedded in the ground near the

▲ Finding places where water may be found is vital in countries affected by drought and famine. Even present-day satellites like Landsat can detect underground water sources and places where crops can grow in desert areas.

▲ Satellites can detect clouds of locusts and other similar insects as they swarm from their breeding grounds. Early warning alerts help pest-control teams wipe out the insects (a locust is shown above) before they totally destroy the crop.

▲ These triangular satellites, each one 300 metres across, are in fact giant mirrors made of reflective aluminium foil. They are designed to focus sunlight onto the nightside of the world. The mirrors' beams could be switched from place to place,

▲ This colour picture shows fields of potatoes. Some of the crop has been affected by blight – diseased potatoes show up black. Satellite views can sometimes detect disease even before the farmer standing in his field.

▲ Forest fires cost thousands of millions of dollars a year in the USA alone. Satellites can be orbited which can detect and provide early warning of forests aflame. In this picture you can see a four-legged walking fire-fighting robot of the future

attacking an outbreak with fire-smothering chemicals. Machines like this, alerted by satellite, could reduce the cost – and danger to life and property – of forest fires. The walking design would enable the robot to fight fires in all sorts of awkward places.

San Andreas fault in Southern California, USA. This zone, which has had major earthquakes before, is a prime candidate for a serious upheaval in the future. Early warnings provided by satellite could save thousands of lives and millions of dollars.

▲ Early warnings, provided by satellites like the one on the left, would enable rescue teams to move quickly into disaster areas. In this picture, a Red Cross hoverjet swoops low over a doomed city to pick up survivors as buildings rock and crumble.

The hoverjet is held aloft by four propellers, shrouded in circular ducts. For forward flight, the ducts swivel through 90 degrees to speed the craft to the nearest hospital. Its maximum speed would be about 450 kph.

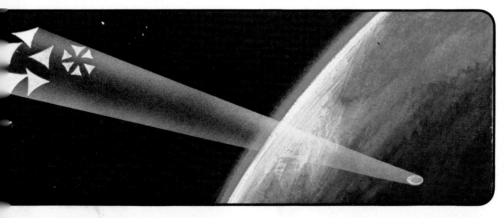

wherever light might be required. On the ground, the mirrors would look like bright stars. The light provided would be about 100 times that of the full moon on a clear night, or about the same as the light level between lamp posts in a present-day city.

Uses for such a system are varied. In a big power-failure, for example, they could be used to illuminate blacked-out towns and cities. They might be used to provide cheap lighting for major road junctions.

▲ This picture shows another use for space mirrors – illuminating fields for farmers to get the harvest in on time. As you can see, although there is enough light to work by, the sky remains completely dark with the stars out as usual.

FARMING ON LAND AND SEA

In 1900 the world's population was 1,550 million. By 2000, it will be rocketing over 6,000 million. The outlook for most of the peoples of the world is hunger or starvation unless food production keeps pace with the number of mouths to feed.

Research into improving soil, crops and animal breeds have produced striking advances in the past. Future improvements will need to avoid pollution through wrongly-used insecticides and soil erosion through over-cultivation.

▲ Meat will be expensive. You can already buy 'extenders' like this cheap soya-bean product. It is mixed into a meat stew to make it go further.

Superfarm, year 2020

Compared with a farm of the present-day, this one seems more like a factory. The high food production required by a vast human population may make factory farms the only way to avoid mass starvation.

1 Farmhouse. Weather reports arrive via satellite; computers keep track of stock and grain yields.
2 Automatic harvester glides along monorail tracks.
3 Helijet sprays fertilizer and weedkiller.
4 Grain is pumped along tubes to nearby city. Old-fashioned trucks are little-used.
5 Many people regard present-day factory farming of animals as cruel and unnecessary even though most housewives are happy to buy cheap factory-farmed chickens. If people still want cheap meat, more of it may have to be produced in this way. Here, cattle are shown in space-saving multi-level pens.
6 Monorail train, loading up with beef.
7 Plastic domes protect crops like tomatoes and strawberries.
8 Orbiting space mirror provides night-lighting to boost crop yield.

Fishfarming the underwater world

At present, man still gets food from the seas in an old-fashioned way – by hunting. This picture shows a better solution – a farm under the water.

1 Globe-shaped farmhouse, warm and dry, equipped with all the comforts of home, plus its own computer systems.
2 Pumping station draws up nutrients from the ocean depths for the fish cages.
3 Aqualung-equipped farmers are helped by dolphins, the sheepdogs of this

underwater world. The nearest farmer has just fired a knockout dart at a stray shark. It will be towed away by a pair of dolphins.
4 Fish farm cage. The walls are made of air bubbles leaked from a pipe system. Fish stay behind the 'wall' as they dislike passing through the bubbles.
5 Farmers poke the suction hose of a fishing boat into a cage. The fish are sucked up into the boat to be gutted and fresh-frozen.

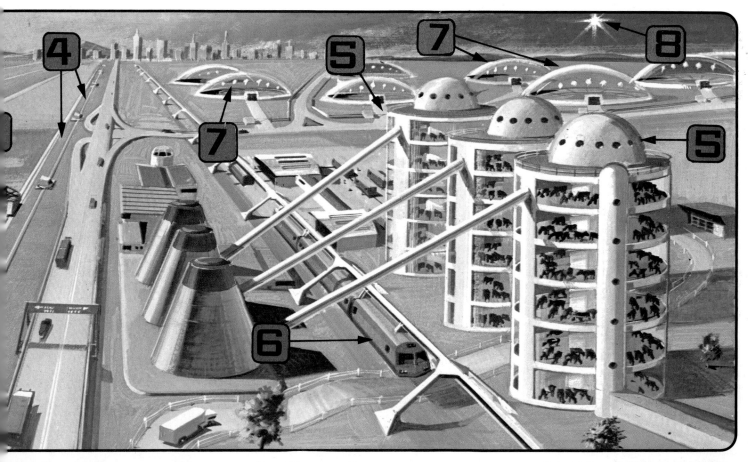

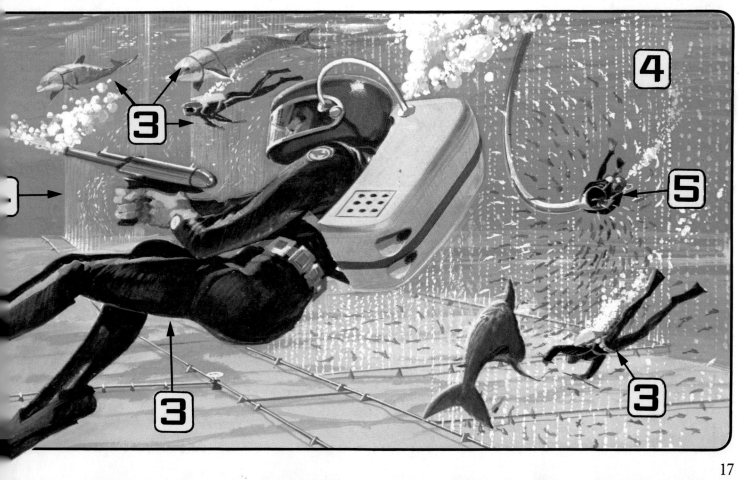

MEDICAL EMERGENCY

Despite advanced telephone and TV equipment and increased fuel prices, people are still going to travel from place to place in the future. The safety and reliability of transport systems is improving and will continue to improve, but no machine (or the person in charge of it) is perfect, or ever will be: accidents will happen.

On these pages you can see the sort of medical help that could be available to help an accident victim, in this case the burnt and broken-boned driver of a turbocar involved in a road smash.

Some of the medical aids are new, others are based on current researches.

1 Rescue services close in on the burning wreck of a turbine-engined car. As fire-fighting robots under the supervision of human firemen lay flame-quenching foam on the car, the nearest heli-ambulance descends to take care of the driver, still trapped inside the vehicle. After he has been cut out of the wreck, he will be airlifted to hospital.

▲ The medics use a spraycan of 'synthetic skin' to treat severe burns. Like man's own skin, the plastic film lets in air to help healing while keeping out bacteria, liquids and dirt. Material like this has already been developed.

▲ The patient is placed in a portable oxygen tent, and his condition is monitored by automatic sensor equipment. The results are radioed to the computer in the hospital awaiting them, providing an up-to-the-minute record of his condition.

The medics oversee the equipment and check all is well. The ambulance is a high-speed craft – once moving forward, its rotor blades slow, then stop to act as wings for fast flight. Flight-control is mainly by robot-pilot.

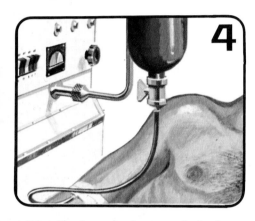

▲ Blood is always in short supply. In the future, artificial blood could be a possibility. Experiments in the USA as early as 1966 proved that 'fluorocarbon' liquids could be used, at least for short periods to replace blood.

5 Preventive medicine, 21st century style

The emphasis in 21st-century medicine will be to prevent most illnesses from becoming serious in the first place, mainly by continuous medical checks from childhood, so that treatment can be administered as soon as any change is noted.

The advantage of this sort of medical treatment is that most people should need much less time in hospital and that medical money and equipment is freed for emergency cases like this one.

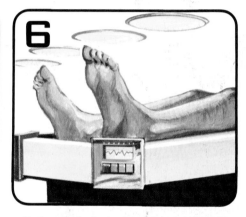

▲ In hospital, the burnt driver is placed on a hoverbed, which suspends him on a gentle cushion of air. As there is no pressure on burn areas, there is less pain and wounds heal more quickly. Dials control hover height and air temperature.

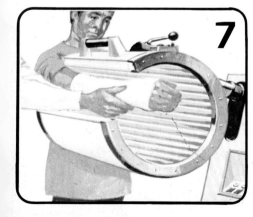

▲ Broken bones are set using plastic tape. It is half the weight of plaster of Paris, three times as strong, and waterproof. After wrapping, the tape is hardened by exposing it to an ultraviolet lamp like the cylindrical one shown above.

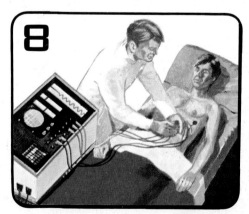

▲ In AD 46, a Roman doctor claimed to cure headaches using current from electric eels. American doctors have already updated the technique with some success. In the 21st century this cure might replace many drugs.

▲ The patient is returned home to familiar surroundings as soon as possible. Just in case of a relapse, he takes home a portable medical analyser which checks and automatically reports on his condition to the hospital computer.

PEOPLE OR MACHINES?

One of the most fantastic achievements of modern medicine has been the transplanting of organs (such as kidneys) from one person to another. Even more startling has been the invention of completely artificial replacements, or implants.

The silhouetted figure below shows the range of transplants and implants which could be put into a body, though it is very unlikely that one person would need them all. Most of the ones shown are already available. Some, such as the nuclear-powered heart have yet to be developed.

It might be possible to achieve near-immortality if organs were continually replaced as they wore out. There could be an unpleasant side-effect though – a black-market in replacement organs.

Exploring a heavy-gravity world in a powered exo-skeleton

This interplanetary explorer of the future has his strength boosted by his robot-like powered 'exo-skeleton'. Developed from present-day prototypes, the suit has a small nuclear reactor to give it the power it needs. Built-in sensors detect and boost the explorer's movements enabling him to walk on a heavy-gravity world (where he would be several times his Earth-weight), lift up large rock samples, and in an emergency run at up to 70 kph.

Key to the cyborg person

With more and more artificial organs available, tomorrow's people might be cyborgs – half human, half robots.

Certainly with the number of replacement organs shown here, the dividing line between man and machine is rather narrow. Parts marked * are not yet available, but soon will be.

1 Skull – made of animal bone
2 Cornea and lens of eye – plastic
3 Eyeball – plastic
4 Nose cartilage – silicone rubber
5 Shoulder joint - vitallium metal
6 Elbow joint – metal
7 Hip joint – a ceramic bone-like material called cerosium
8 Artery – dacron plastic tubing
9 Ear cartilage – silicone rubber
10 Jawbone – cerosium
11 Blood pressure regulator – electronic
12 Trachea (air passage) – silicone rubber
13 Lung – silicone rubber *
14 Heart – silicone rubber, nuclear powered *
15 Liver – transplant *
16 Kidney – transplant
17 Finger joints – metal
18 Bladder stimulator – electronic
19 Thighbone and knee joint – metal
20 Foot tendon – silicone rubber

ARTIFICIAL INTELLIGENCE

Many computer engineers are convinced that we are seeing the evolution of a new species – that of the intelligent machine.

Already chess-playing computers can beat all but a handful of human opponents. Although computers have to be programmed with instructions by people, it is possible to foresee the time when they will learn and react without instruction – then it will be one small step to 'intelligence'.

It took Nature many millions of years to evolve the human brain. Now that same biological creation is creating an offspring. The process may take just a few decades. Then the first true robots may walk the Earth.

▲ The first electronic computer went into operation in 1943. Using bulky valves in its circuits it sprawled across 160 square metres. In the 1950s small transistors replaced valves and a modern computer like the one above takes up only a few metres. The latest computers have transistors in 'micro-chip' form reducing the size of their electronic 'brains' thousands of times. Computers are good at arithmetic, but they cannot (as yet) think for themselves.

Computer counting

1	1	110	6
10	2	111	7
11	3	1000	8
100	4	1001	9
101	5	1010	10

Computers count in binary code. The binary equivalents of decimal numbers are shown here. See if you can work out this word, coded into binary – 1010 1 10. Answer, page 32.

▲ Smaller and smaller is the trend in computer design. This picture, looking a bit like an aerial view of a city, is in fact an enlarged view of a micro circuit infused on a wafer-thin chip of silicon just 63 mm across. Silicon chips are already used in, for example, calculators and clocks. In the future, chip equipped machines are going to take over routine jobs from humans on a massive scale in the same way that machines took over from human muscles 200 years before.

▲ This picture shows a computer at work in the car industry. Designers have the car's shape displayed on a TV screen. The image can be viewed from any angle and changed easily until the body style is decided upon making designing quicker and cheaper.

▲ Civilization is becoming increasingly dependent on computers. As machines take over, society becomes more vulnerable to natural or man-made disasters. If power supplies are interrupted, industries and cities, like the blacked-out town above, grind to a halt. Unless people retain basic skills and crafts, parts or all of civilization could perish. Perhaps groups of craft workers could be set up as an insurance policy against global disaster.

Man and machine — partners down the future ages

The prospect of intelligent machines should be little cause for fear. A man/machine partnership, each doing what it is best at, is more likely than that of mad robots taking over the world.

The result could be just another step along the pathway of human evolution, perhaps an entirely new breed of man, better fitted to explore the Universe.

This picture shows a possible exploration team of the future. Humans and machines work together as they study a small inhabitant of a world far away in the depths of space. In this explorer team the humans are 'in charge', though the starship's electronic brain has more capacity than the brains of all its human crew put together, and would probably override (or at least query) any orders it disagreed with.

The human-shaped machine, a true 'robot' is possible, but likely to be an unusual member in the ranks of the robots. Designed and built for specific functions, few robots will need exactly the same number or type of limbs as a human being.

BATTLEGROUND 2000

One prediction of the future is, unfortunately, fairly certain – battles, large and small will continue to be fought in trouble-spots across the world.

East versus West rivalry will continue and weapons development will continue too. On this page, you can see some of the fighting machines that could join battle towards the end of the century.

Weapons development is not all bad however – for example, ultra-reliable robotic computer systems designed for the heat of battle are also used in airliners across the world, making flying safer.

▼ The Rockwell HiMAT is an advanced fighter concept, designed for dogfighting in the 1990s. The HiMAT is shown below compared in size with a World War II Mustang fighter. On the right, it is locked in combat with an enemy craft.

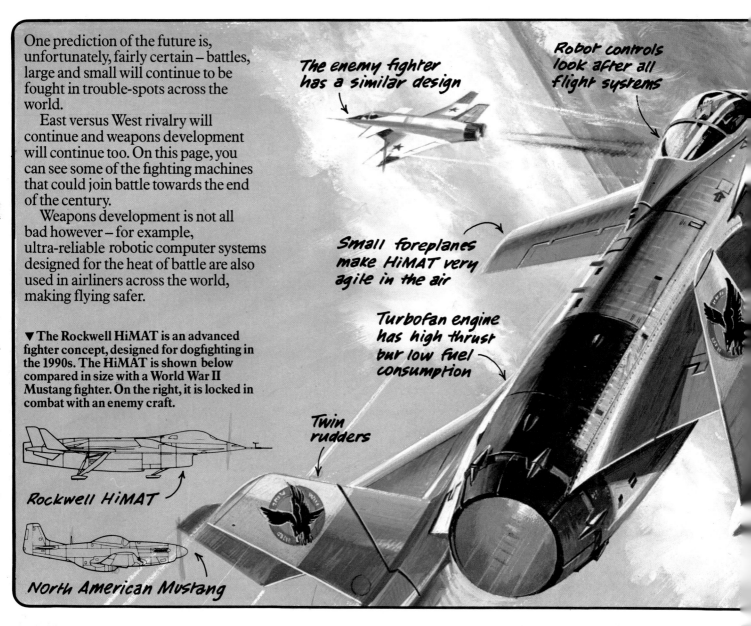

The enemy fighter has a similar design

Robot controls look after all flight systems

Small foreplanes make HiMAT very agile in the air

Turbofan engine has high thrust but low fuel consumption

Twin rudders

Rockwell HiMAT

North American Mustang

Rocket troops of the future

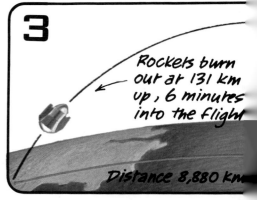

Rockets burn out at 131 km up, 6 minutes into the flight

Distance 8,880 km

▲ It is night-time, as troops prepare to board a giant rocket transport. Their task – to quell an uprising in a state half-way across the world. The rocket is fuelled with liquid hydrogen and liquid oxygen and is ready to go.

▲ Lift-off. The troops are pressed down in their couches during the high acceleration vertical climb. In just over five minutes, the transport is nearly 100 km up and still climbing, up and out into space. The whole flight is completely robot-controlled.

▲ As the craft climbs, it tilts over into an arching curve to carry it toward the far side of the Earth. The outer, hydrogen-carrying, tanks are dropped when their fuel is used up after six minutes of flight. The transport coasts up to a maximum height of more

Single nose-mounted laser-cannon

Robot missiles are of the 'fire and forget' type. Once released, they home in on the target by themselves with no further aiming by the pilot

▲ Although not powerful enough at present, the laser 'death ray' is eventually going to be a standard weapon. Here an armoured car carries one in place of the shell-firing cannon that it would be armed with today.

▲ Hovercraft will carry troops up the beaches in future amphibious assaults. The hovercraft above is powered by twin turbines to thrust it along at speeds up to 100 kph. Its nose drops down to form a landing ramp.

▲ 100-kph hydrofoil patrol boats already exist in small numbers. By the 1990s most, if not all, world navies will be equipped with them. The one above is firing one of several anti-shipping missiles carried in the tubes at the stern. Missiles like this make battleships and aircraft carriers easy to attack. Few navies will want the giant ships in the future. Small hydrofoils cannot stay at sea very long, so submarines will be used to refuel and re-arm them away from their shore bases.

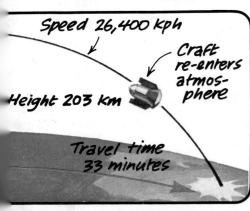

Speed 26,400 kph

Craft re-enters atmos-phere

Height 203 km

Travel time 33 minutes

than 200 km, well out of the Earth's atmosphere. It re-enters blunt tail first, using it as an Apollo-style heat-shield. In just over half an hour it will have covered nearly 9,000 km at an amazing average speed of 16,650 kph.

4

▲ After a period of weightlessness during the coasting part of the flight, the troops are again pressed into their couches as the craft hits the atmosphere. A shockwave curves away from the heatshield during re-entry.

5

▲ It is dawn as the transporter lands. Armed hovercars nose out of the cargo hold to lay a cordon round the transport before the main body of troops move off to deal with the uprising. The transporter acts as a command base for the operation.

SPEAKING TO THE STARS

Is Mankind alone in the Universe? To try and find out, astronomers have begun a search for radio signals which may have been sent by beings living on other worlds. The search began in 1960 when Dr Frank Drake used a radio telescope in the USA to listen to the stars Tau Ceti and Epsilon Eridani.

There were no tell-tale signals from other civilizations. Had there been, we may have discovered something of their science, but conversation would have been painfully slow. Radio signals would take nearly 12 years to reach us from Tau Ceti and a similar time for the replies from Earth-based transmitters to travel back.

▲ Space probes fast enough to leave the Solar System carry messages in case alien spacefarers find them millions of years in the future. Pioneers 10 and 11 (shown above) each carry an aluminium plaque showing human beings, the space craft, the planets of the Solar System and its position in the Galaxy. Two Voyager probes carry disc recordings which tell the story of life on Earth in words and sounds, from the crashing of waves and the grunts of animals to the cry of a baby.

The space-based superscope

One day a giant radio telescope like this may float above the world. Built in space by astronauts and robots, its immense antenna will receive signals from the depths of the Universe. Far more sensitive than any radio telescope on Earth, it may catch whispers from alien civilizations sent out thousands of years before.

▲ This is the radio telescope used by Dr Drake in 1960. Near Arecibo in Puerto Rico is a still larger one, over 300 metres across. In 1974 it was used to transmit a message to Messier 13, a star cluster on the edge of our galaxy.

▲ Messier 13 contains about 300,000 stars, some of which may have planets with alien creatures on them. So remote is the cluster that the message, containing information about ourselves, will take 24,000 years to get there.

Was anybody there?

What kind of creatures might receive messages from Earth? There is no way to tell, so this picture is totally fictitious. The aliens, though highly intelligent, look little like human beings. Their radio telescope is not too different though – designed for the same purpose, it has a family resemblance to those of Earth. The radio message the aliens are puzzling over tells of life on Earth. If the creatures live in the Messier 13 cluster, they are about to find out what life was like on Earth thousands of years in their past.

What happens if we contact alien beings – and they are far in advance of the human race?

Some think the result would be an exciting era of adventure and discovery. Others argue, 'Would people struggle to achieve breakthroughs in arts and science if they had the feeling that it had all been done before? A sort of racial laziness, and ultimately death, could be the result'.

Perhaps if there are aliens out there, they will not reply until they think the human race can stand the shock of contact.

What do you think – would contact be an adventure ... or a disaster?

MIND OVER MATTER-THE FINAL FRONTIER

Many people believe that, in addition to the ordinary human senses of sight, smell, taste, touch and hearing, a sixth sense lies waiting to be developed. They call it extra-sensory perception or simply ESP. It includes different abilities, such as telepathy (the ability to communicate thoughts mind to mind) and telekinesis (the ability to move objects by an act of will without touching them).

Scientists have tried to prove the reality of these and other 'strange powers' in many experiments, so far without conclusive evidence for or against. Future research should solve the problem. Could machines use ESP too? Only time will tell.

▲ When astronaut Edgar Mitchell flew to the Moon in Apollo 14, he tried to communicate telepathically with friends on Earth. His duties aboard ship sometimes interfered with his experiments but ESP-investigator Dr J. B. Rhine thought the results encouraging. Perhaps better results could be achieved if ESP could be tried on a distant planet, far from the 'telepathic interference' of the millions of other brains on Earth. Eventually mechanical ESP-boosters might be built for anyone to use.

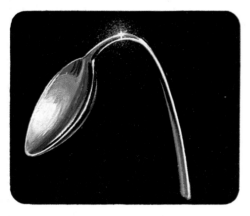

▲ Yuri Geller and others claim to bend metal objects by the power of thought. It seems like magic, but if such things can be done (and there is no proof that they can), they work because of the effect of an as yet undiscovered law of nature.

▲ There are many cases in which objects like tea cups and flower vases have suddenly – and inexplicably – taken off and smashed against walls or floors. This 'poltergeist' activity could be an example of telekinesis in action.

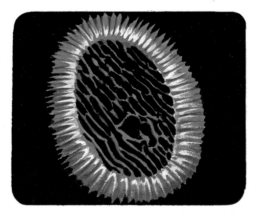

▲ Can a person heal another by the 'laying on of hands'? If so, special Kirlian photographs like this one may show the process. Streams of light surround the hand. As healing takes place, the finger tips appear to flare brightly.

Try your own telepathy experiment

Make a set of cards marked with a square, circle, cross and three wavy lines. These are the standard symbols used by professional researchers, though you can use others of your own choosing, such as the triangle shown on the right.

Choose a card at random, frame the symbol in your mind and try to 'think' it to a friend in a room next door. Russian researchers tried an experiment like this between Moscow and the science city of Novosibirsk which are 11,000 km apart. They claimed 12 of the 25 symbols were received correctly, far too many to be coincidence. See how many you get.

The ESPER battlecruiser

In the distant future people may be doing things that would seem like magic to us. Our descendants may have created bionic men and women able to boost the power of their minds to fantastic levels with mechanical robotic ESP-boosters.

In this picture, a star war is being fought with a ship crewed by ESP sensitives. Mind-power communicates with the distant Starbase. Machines and weapons are thought-controlled. The captain, hooked into the Battle Computer, has only to *think* his tactics – and they happen. Like the spoonbenders of today, he may have the power to distort metal in the enemy craft and destroy their weapons. In the ship's hospital, healing hands and minds take care of battle casualties.

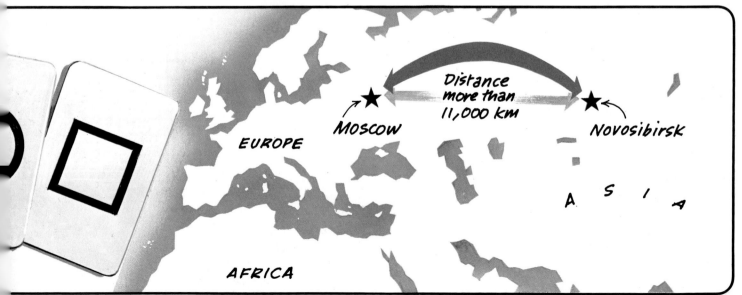

Distance more than 11,000 km

EUROPE

Moscow

Novosibirsk

A S I A

AFRICA

THE NEXT 120 YEARS: A TIMECHART

Visionaries of the late 19th and early 20th centuries like Jules Verne and H. G. Wells predicted many of the inventions which have since changed the world, including submarines, aeroplanes, spacecraft and trips to the Moon.

Even bigger changes can be expected in the next 100 years. Provided that a major atomic war can be avoided, the foreseeable future is likely to be very exciting.

Here are just some of the things which might happen, most of them within your lifetime.

1980-1990

Space telescope launched by Space Shuttle into Earth orbit. The 13 metre-long telescope enables astronomers to view stars seven times further away and 50 times fainter than possible using telescopes on Earth.

Space Shuttle demonstrates large solar-power unit as a demonstrator for the Satellite Solar Power Station.

High-energy lasers are tested in space. They are intended as weapons to disable enemy satellites.

Solar power plants set up in the Middle East to help provide cheap power for farmers.

Girder-beam building equipment tested in orbit; demonstrates ability to construct huge lightweight structures like the SSPS using automatic robots.

Wave machines developed in Britain used to produce electricity in coastal areas.

Experimental nuclear-fusion power station generates electricity successfully.

Orbital space station demonstrates that many industrial processes are cheaper and better carried out in space.

1991-2000

HiMAT-type fighters in service. Some equipped with robot pilots, flying automatically and able to fly tougher and longer missions than human pilots.

High-power lasers become standard issue on the battlefield, replacing many guns and cannon.

Reign of the robot draws near as the machine functions of vision, movement, manipulation and 'thinking' are steadily improved.

Earthquake detector flown into orbit by Space Shuttle. Used to check the unstable San Andreas fault in California, USA.

Fire-fighting machines equipped with robot command systems used in the USA to help combat forest fires.

Microcell surgery – the ability to destroy individual diseased cells in the body using laser beams – is widely practised in hospitals.

Undersea fish farms built to improve fish stocks in the oceans.

Computer systems are developed which learn from their mistakes like humans.

High-speed hovercraft troop-carriers replace most ordinary assault craft in the world's navies.

Genetic engineering, the artificial improvement of plant or animal breeds, is used to make super-strains of wheat, corn, barley, maize and many other food crops. Better resistance to disease and bigger plants help to feed the peoples of the world.

Industrial robots increasingly take over the jobs of skilled engineers in factories.

The Replicator is developed. The device can make practically anything using material from chemicals stored nearby. The complex instructions required are masterminded by computer; laser beams place atoms and molecules into position to build any object.

Space mirrors placed in orbit to provide night-lighting on Earth. Uses of the sunlight-reflecting mirrors include city lighting and as floodlights in emergency situations like earthquake relief work.

2001-2050

First nuclear-fusion power station goes into commercial service in the USA. Obtains power from deuterium extracted from sea water.

Second-generation Space Shuttles used to carry materials into space factory orbit. Similar craft able to carry troops across the world. Boeing HLV design uses giant lake to land in back on Earth.

Micro-processor mini-robot implanted in human brain. Machine helps stroke victims regain the use of their arms and legs, replacing the lost nerves.

Robots and astronauts construct first Satellite Solar Power Station in orbit. The SSPS beams a continuous beam of microwave energy to receiving stations on Earth.

Fusion power converted into microwave energy; 'exported' to other countries using a relay satellite to beam the microwaves around the world.

Men return to the Moon for the first time since 1973. This time they are surveyors, prospecting for the best site for a Moonmining colony.

Robot mining equipment landed on the Moon to extract metals from rock.

Electromagnetic catapult built on the Moon to launch raw materials to Earth-orbit space factories and to construct other habitats in space.

Robot survey craft lands on an asteroid to check its mineral worth.

Giant radio-telescope placed into Earth orbit. Its task – to search for signs of other life in the Universe, intelligent life which might be broadcasting radio signals.

Asteroids used as source of mineral wealth. Small mining colonies in the Asteroid Belt are the start of an 'Outer Solar System' human civilization.

2051-2099

Faint signals received from space by orbiting radio-telescope. Mystery radio-waves thought to be coded message from alien creatures.

Space mirrors, under strict United Nations control, start weather-control experiments.

Computer systems effectively run the world. Only robot machine intelligence can keep track of complex problems of running a planet inhabited by 6-7,000 million people.

Practically all factory jobs taken over by industrial robots.

Scientists and super computer decode the signals from the stars received years before. First results are breakthroughs in science frontiers using the information contained in the message.

Great interest in alien message leads to the research and development of star-travelling spacecraft

Jupiter's atmosphere mined with robot controlled balloon stations. Materials used by the human colonies now based in Earth orbit, on the Moon, Mars, and in the Asteroid Belt.

THE 22ND CENTURY AND BEYOND

Third Industrial Revolution complete: virtually all polluting industries either cleaned up or moved out into space. Man and machine gradually turn Planet Earth back into an ecologically-balanced garden planet.

Cyborgs in general use. Half-robots combining micro-electronics, power machinery and parts of human beings perform tasks impossible for humans alone.

Using computer-power and deep-space research stations, the mysteries of human ESP senses are solved. Robot ESP-boosters developed; used as brain implants for anyone who want to be an ESP-sensitive.

Artificial computer intelligence exceeds that of humans. The super robot concentrates on helping humans achieve more with the limited brain power available to them. Human adaptability makes for a man/machine partnership to explore the Universe. The birth of a new super-race.

INDEX

GLOSSARY

ALIEN Stranger or foreigner. In this book the word refers to creatures from another planet.

APOLLO Spaceship that took astronauts to the Moon.

ASTEROID BELT Thousands of small rocks orbiting in space between Mars and Jupiter.

BLOOD CLOTTING Thickening of blood that happens when you cut yourself. As it solidifies, it seals the cut.

GALAXY Giant cluster of stars. Our own galaxy, the Milky Way, contains about 100,000 million stars.

ION DRIVE System of powering spacecraft using electrically charged particles to provide thrust.

LASER Intense beam of light, used for a variety of purposes such as cutting, welding and as a replacement for radio communications.

PIONEER SPACEPROBES In 1973, Pioneer 10 was sent to take photographs of Jupiter. Pioneer 11 is aimed at Saturn. Both craft will eventually leave the Solar System.

POLLUTION Waste in the wrong place, causing harmful side-effects.

SENSOR Device to 'sense' or gather information about its surroundings.

SOLAR SYSTEM The planets, moons, asteroids and comets which orbit around the Sun.

SPEED OF LIGHT Just under 300,000 kilometres a second. A light year is the distance light travels in a year.

VOYAGER SPACEPROBES Two craft launched in 1978, both aimed towards Jupiter and Saturn. Voyager 2 may later be redirected to pass near Uranus and Neptune.

Computer counting answer

The word is JAB. It has been programmed into binary using the system 1 = A, 2 = B, and so on. People can use different coding systems (called programmes) depending on the problem they are working on.